Eating Rainbows

BY FAITH ST. CLAIR

ILLUSTRATED BY WENDY WILSON SPOONER

ISBN: 978-1-7368127-0-9

I was sick in bed and couldn't play.

I couldn't dance or

run or

jump .

I couldn't tumble or even swim .

I hurt too much, and my tube got in the way.

I didn't sing today.

I didn't talk or

whistle or

giggle .

I didn't shout hurray

or even growl.

I hurt too much, and my tube got in the way.

I tried to eat
my favorite things.

I tried to eat apples

and strawberries

and avocados .

I tried to eat crackers and even cake.

But I hurt too much. and my tube got in the way.

So, I sat on my porch and took a deep breath

of the outside air.

The sun tickled my face

and made me warm .

Until it r
a
i
n
e
d.
And I was cold.

But then it stopped, and the sun came back

to visit me.

He brought a friend.

His colors looked so fun and happy and yummy.

So, I sat on my porch and ate

the rainbow.

At first,

I just licked it,

one color at a time

Then I took big delicious bites.

I did not hurt, and my tube did not get in the way.

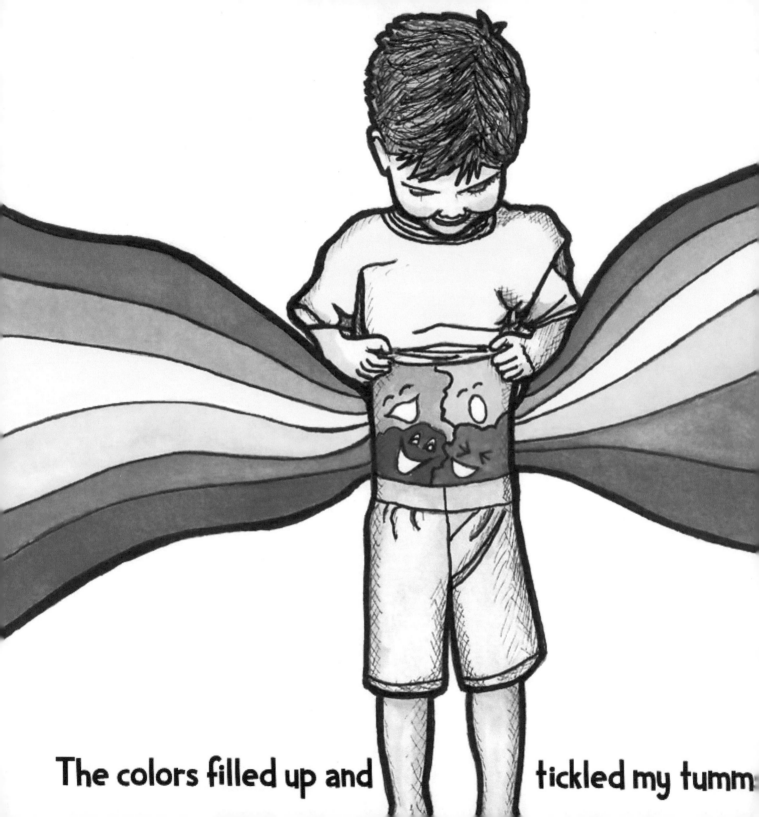

The colors filled up and   tickled my tumm

They sang and ♪ ♫ giggled and shouted hurray!

They danced and jumped and swam and ran around.

I felt warm and happy inside.

I played and sang and

ate a rainbow today!

RESOURCES

Points to Ponder

Frustrations

Fears

Inclusion

Happy Places

Conversation Questions

What are some things you **can't** do, even if you wanted to?

How does that make you feel?

What are some things you just **don't** feel like doing even when you can?

How does that make you feel when you decide not to do them?

What are some things you have **tried** to do, but it didn't turn out well when you tried to do them?

How did that make you feel when things didn't go so well?

What did you notice that was different about the little boy in the story?

Do you have questions about that?

If you wanted to ask the little boy a question, how do you think you could do that in a respectful way?

What would you ask? (Does it hurt?)

How do feel about including everyone--even those who are different?

Application Questions

What makes you happy and feel warm inside?

What are some of your favorite things that make you happy?

Who are some of your favorite people that make you happy?

What are some of your favorite activities that make you happy?

Do you have favorite words or songs that make you happy?

Observation Questions

How did the sun make him feel?

How did the rain make him feel?

How did the rainbow make him feel?

What color is the dancing color?

What color is the running color?

What color is the jumping color?

What color is the swimming color?

What color is the playing color?

What color is the singing color?

What color is the shouting color?

What color is the growling color?

What color is the warm color?

What color is the happy color?

What color is the shouting hurray color?

What color is the giggling color?

What color is the talking color?

What color is the whistling color?

What color is the tumbling color?

What do you think you can do when you are feeling sad because you can't do something?

How can you help someone else be happy when they are sad or frustrated or feeling left out?

Singing

Painting

A friend

Animals

What is your rainbow?

Praying

Sunshine

Mountains

Flowers

Family

Books

Running

Each of us can find something we can turn to that fills us up
with rainbows and allows us to find happiness even
despite our limitations.

CPSIA information can be obtained
at www.ICGtesting.com
Printed in the USA
BVHW021344080421
604484BV00011B/254